1 2 3 4 5

Panda's Counting Adventure

6 7 8 9 10

one

One panda is going
on an adventure.

What is he flying in?

1 2 3 4 5 6 7 8 9 10

two

Two elephants are doing circus tricks.

What color is the flag?

1 **2** 3 4 5 6 7 8 9 10

three

Three whales are swimming in the ocean.

Are they happy or sad?

1 2 **3** 4 5 6 7 8 9 10

four

Four lions are singing.

What sounds do lions usually make?

1 2 3 **4** 5 6 7 8 9 10

five

Five polar bears are having a snowball fight.

What color are the polar bears?

5

1 2 3 4 **5** 6 7 8 9 10

six

Six alligators are taking a nap.

Can you spot the one that just woke up?

1 2 3 4 5 6 7 8 9 10

seven

Seven penguins are riding a wave.

What colors are Panda and the penguins?

1 2 3 4 5 6 7 8 9 10

eight

Eight camels are walking through the desert.

Is the desert a hot or a cold place?

8

1 2 3 4 5 6 7 **8** 9 10

nine

Nine spiders are climbing up a wall.

Who is already at the top of the wall?

1 2 3 4 5 6 7 8 9 10

ten

Ten snakes are happy to see Panda!

Can you find the snakes that have spots?

1 2 3 4 5 6 7 8 9 10

This edition published in 2014
by SpiceBox™
12171 Horseshoe Way
Richmond, BC
Canada V7A 4V4

First published in 2014
Copyright © SpiceBox™ 2014

ISBN 10: 1-77132-278-0
ISBN 13: 978-1-77132-278-2

CEO & Publisher: Ben Lotfi
Editorial: Ania Jaraczewski
Creative Director: Garett Chan
Art Director: Christine Covert
Design & Layout: Kimberly Ang
Production: James Badger, Mell D'Clute
Sourcing: Tony Su, Shirley Chan

For more SpiceBox products and information,
visit our website:
www.spiceboxbooks.com

Manufactured in China

1 3 5 7 9 10 8 6 4 2